EYEBEAM

TEETERING ON THE BLINK

by Sam Hurt

★
TexasMonthlyPress

Other books by Sam Hurt:
I'm Pretty Sure I've Got My Death-Ray in Here Somewhere!
Eyebeam, Therefore I Am
Eenie Meenie Minie Tweed
Our Eyebeams Twisted
The Mind's Eyebeam

Small Print Page

Texas Monthly Press
P.O. Box 1569
Austin, Texas 78767

A   B   C   D   E   F   G   H

Printed in the U.S.ofA.

Newspapers and individual Beamofanatics: Keep up with *Eyebeam* through New Stream Comics, P.O. Box 893, Austin, Texas, 78767. Contact Chuck Higdon (512) 343-0418.

Library of Congress Cataloging-in-Publication Data

Hurt, Sam.
    Eyebeam, teetering on the Blink.

    I. Title.   II. Title: Eyebeam.
PN6728.E94H86   1988   741.5'973   88-2251
ISBN 0-87719-100-X (pbk.)

This book is intended for mature adults only. Children are advised not to allow immature adults to read it without careful supervision. The characters and events portrayed in this work are fictional. Any resemblance to actual persons or events results from the fact that the whole thing is based on your life and the people you know. This is only possible because you are the only real person existing. Everyone and everything else is an illusion. Apparently, it's all part of some big experiment or something. This is a book of cartoons, not an eyechart. Please turn the page.

Many people provided advice and criticism on the cover of this book. The ink-slinger would like to thank a few of those who were particularly helpful: Bill Barnett, Sam Hurt, Jr., Howard Wimberley, and Jun Hurt (who has to look at a lot of ink).

Thanks to Chuck Higdon for help in getting all these pages into one place.

Artistical acknowledgments to Quino, Crumb, and Seuss.

Thanks to Bob Thaves, Mike Peters, Jerry Van Amerongen, Berke Breathed, and Steve O'Donnell for going out of their way to treat me as a colleague in the field of humor management. Thanks to Dan Shefelman for actually being a colleague. Thanks to Matt Groening for letting me draw Binky. Buddy Hickerson, I still owe you a drawing. Thanks to Ben Sargent for friendship, guidance, and white-out. Thanks to Mom for reading this far to see if I mentioned her, too.

EYEBEAM

1

2

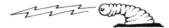

EXEBEAM

Panel 1: I SAW THE WEIRDEST THING ON PBS... APPARENTLY, THERE HAVE BEEN STRANGE INCIDENCES WHERE **FISH** RAINED DOWN FROM THE SKY.

OH YES THE UNEXPLAINED.... LIKE SPONTANEOUS HUMAN COMBUSTION. - OR THE MARFA LIGHTS...

Panel 2: WHAT ABOUT THE STATUES ON EASTER ISLAND? HOW'D THEY **GET** THERE? WHY DID THE DINOSAURS DISAPPEAR?

WE MAY NEVER KNOW.

ON THOSE SUPER SUGAR CRISP COMMERCIALS, THE VOICE OF "SUGAR BEAR" HAS NEVER SOUNDED **QUITE** THE **SAME** SINCE BING CROSBY DIED...

©87 SAM HURT

HEY, SALLY- COME LOOK AT THIS - RATLIFF IS LOST IN THOUGHT.

HE PROBABLY STARTED OUT TRYING TO CHOOSE A CAREER AND WOUND UP MIRED IN AN ATTEMPT TO DEFINE HIS SELF IMAGE.

...OR MAYBE HE STARTED OUT TRYING TO CHOOSE A CAREER AND WOUND UP ADRIFT IN AN OCEAN OF POSSIBILITIES, LOSING HIS SENSE OF DIRECTION...

LET'S LET HIM BROOD IN PEACE.

... BUT, ON THE OTHER HAND, ASTRONAUTS MIGHT **NOT** GET COFFEE BREAKS...

©87 Sam Hurt

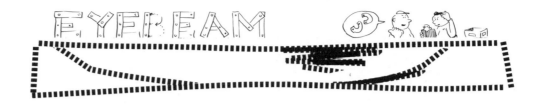

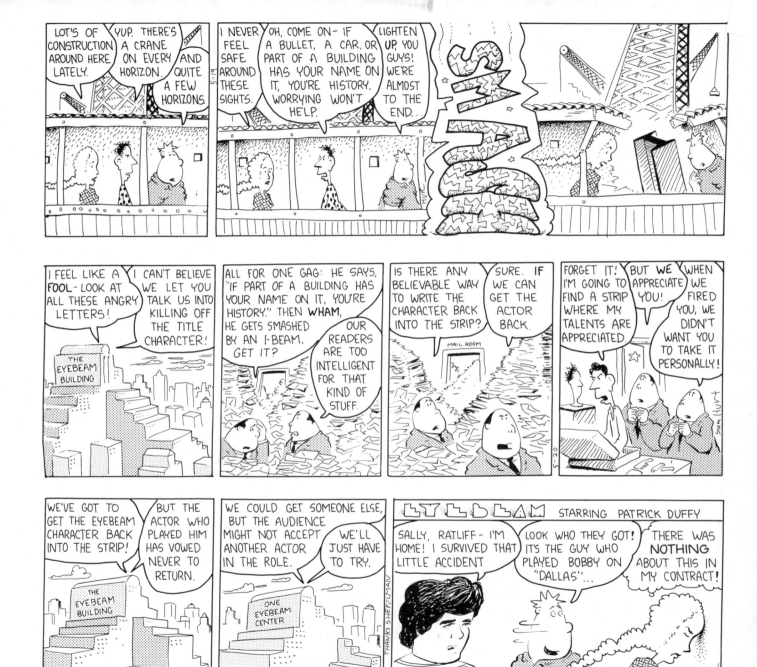

IDOL THREATS

21

Panel 1: IS RATLIFF STILL IN ADVERTISING? / THAT'S A WILCO. IF YOU WANT TO SEE THE LATEST DEVELOPMENT, TURN AROUND...

Panel 2: HE'S THE ONE WHO STANDS APART EVEN FROM HIS OWN CROWD. THE DIFFERENT DRUMMERS HAVE ALWAYS MARCHED TO HIS BEAT... / IT'S HIM! HE'S "THE MAN IN THE LOUD BATHROBE." / THE FASHION STATEMENT THAT ANSWERS A LOT OF QUESTIONS NOBODY WAS EVER GOING TO ASK.

Panel 3: SO TELL ME ABOUT THIS NEW JOB, RATLIFF— WHAT DOES "THE MAN IN THE LOUD BATHROBE" DO? / OH, MOSTLY I JUST EMANATE A RUGGED INDIVIDUALISM.

Panel 4: SOUNDS EASY. WHAT'S IT PAY? / WAIT. THAT'S NOT ALL. I ALSO HAVE TO EXUDE AN ALOOF DISREGARD FOR PASSING TRENDS...

Panel 5: I GUESS IT DOES ADD UP... / I HAVE TO DISPLAY AN UNDERSTANDING THAT THE EXTRA MONEY YOU SPEND ON QUALITY APPAREL GETS YOU GREATER VALUE...

Panel 6: WOW. THAT'S QUITE A FEAT! / ESPECIALLY SINCE I'M THE STRONG SILENT TYPE— IT ALL HAS TO SHOW IN MY EYES. / OH GOD NO! —JUST WHEN YOU THOUGHT IT WAS SAFE TO GET OUT OF THE BATHTUB!

Panel 7: WHEN THE BEAUTIFUL PEOPLE GATHER, THERE'S ONE TOPIC THAT ALWAYS SEEMS TO COME UP. / HE'S HERE! I SAW HIM. / BUT, I HEARD HE WAS IN MONTE CARLO.

Panel 8: IT'S THAT CERTAIN SOMEONE, THE ONE WHO DRIFTS THROUGH A PARTY LIKE A RUMOR OR THE FAINT AROMA OF MUSK... / THEY SAY HE JUST GOT BACK FROM MONTE CARLO. / I HEAR HE SPENDS A LOT OF TIME THERE.

Panel 9: IT'S THE PIED-PIPER OF THE INTERNATIONAL JET-SET: "THE MAN IN THE LOUD BATHROBE." / DON'T TURN AROUND, SYLVIA, HE'S RIGHT BEHIND YOU. / COCKTAIL, SIR? / MAYBE LATER. RIGHT NOW I'M STEERING THE COURSE FOR A WHOLE NEW GENERATION.

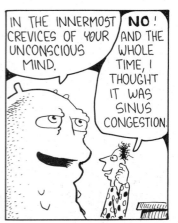

Panel 1:
SQAD LEADER TO INVASION FORCES: LOOK AT YOUR DISPLAY SCREEN FOR FURTHER INFORMATION ABOUT THE TARGET PLANET...

SQAD LEADER

HEY! THAT'S NOT ME BROADCASTING!

Panel 2:

...THIS SPECIMEN REPRESENTS THE SPECIES WE ARE ABOUT TO DESTROY. KNOWN AS WILLIAM "THE REFRIGERATOR" PERRY, HE IS SHOWN HERE WITH HIS INFANT DAUGHTER.

HOW CAN WE DO THIS? HAVE WE NO SHAME?

Sam Hurt 5-6

Panel 3:

INVASION CANCELLED.

LET'S GO HOME.

SEE? EVEN THE MOST EVIL OF ROBOT HORDES HAVE A SOFT SPOT FOR ANYONE NAMED AFTER A HOUSEHOLD APPLIANCE.

Panel 4:

HEY- WHAT ARE WE **DOING**? WE CAN'T JUST PACK UP AND HEAD HOME JUST BECAUSE SOMEONE SHOWS US A CUTE PICTURE...

Sam Hurt 5-7

Panel 5:

WHAT OF OUR **ORDERS**? WHAT OF DUTY? **INVASION FORCE**: ABOUT **FACE**! - BACK TO THE TARGET PLANET! LET'S GET 'EM THIS TIME!

PLAN B.

Z Z Z Z Z

31

AH. SO **NOW** HE SHOWS UP, JUST IN TIME TO JOIN IN ON THE FESTIVITIES!

NOPE. THERE'S NOTHING LIKE GIVING A PARTY WHEN YOU HAVE TO MAKE ALL THE PREPARATIONS YOURSELF.

HEY, THERE'S A METEOR SHOWER OUTSIDE!

HAVE SOME HORS D'OEUVRES. THEY'RE NOT AS FANCY AS I USUALLY MAKE, BUT THAT'S JUST THE WAY IT GOES....

MMMM!

...WHEN CERTAIN INDIVIDUALS NEVER DO THEIR PART.

SEE IF I SAVE **YOUR** PLANET NEXT TIME, DIP-BREATH.

SUNRISE ON UTILITARIA. WHAT AN INSPIRING SIGHT. -AND INSPIRATION IS THE ONLY THING WE EVER RUN SHORT ON.

AFTER SURPASSING ALL OTHER CIVILIZATIONS, WE LOST OUR SENSE OF PURPOSE. WITH NO ONE LEFT TO SHOW UP, OUR TECHNOLOGY WAS IN DANGER OF BECOMING MEAN-INGLESS, SO WE STARTED USING IT TO ERADICATE THE COMPETITION...

THAT ONE PLANET, EARTH, SEEMED KINDA INTRIGUING, THOUGH... SEEMED LIKE A SHAME TO WASTE IT. BUT HEY- I'M NOT ONE TO STAND IN THE WAY OF PROGRESS...

BESIDES, WHEN THEY GET THE WHOLE THING PAVED, IT'LL BE THE EASIEST PLACE IN THE GALAXY TO FIND A PARKING PLACE.

Panel 1: SIRE— A MEMBER OF THE EARTH INVASION FORCE HAS ARRIVED... / SEND IT IN. I'VE BEEN WONDERING WHAT HAPPENED TO THAT MISSION.

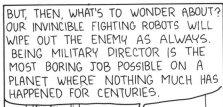

Panel 2: BUT, THEN, WHAT'S TO WONDER ABOUT? OUR INVINCIBLE FIGHTING ROBOTS WILL WIPE OUT THE ENEMY AS ALWAYS. BEING MILITARY DIRECTOR IS THE MOST BORING JOB POSSIBLE ON A PLANET WHERE NOTHING MUCH HAS HAPPENED FOR CENTURIES.

Panel 3: TOTALLY... WIPED OUT... ONLY... CHOKE.... SURVIVOR... GASP... / AFTER ALL THESE YEARS, THE PLOT THICKENS!...

Panel 4: AMBUSH... MASSACRE... UNANTICIPATED TECHNOLOGY... / INCREDIBLE! EARTH HAS DEALT US THE FIRST MILITARY DEFEAT UTILITARIA HAS SUFFERED IN A GENERATION!...

Panel 5: ...A GENERATION OF GENERAL MALAISE AND LACK OF COMMITMENT, WHEN OUR CIVILIZATION HAD NO SENSE OF ITSELF— NO DIRECTION. BUT NOW, SUDDENLY THERE'S SOMEONE TO WORRY ABOUT... SOMEONE TO KEEP UP WITH...

Panel 6: HEY, EVERYBODY, THE JONESES ARE BACK! / PLANETARY ADDRESS SYSTEM

Panel 7: THE INHABITANTS OF UTILITARIA THINK THEY'VE FINALLY BEEN OUT-DONE TECHNOLOGICALLY. THEY HAVE A NEW RIVAL TO RESPECT AND EMULATE. THEY TURN THEIR ANTENNAE TOWARDS EARTH.

Panel 8: BECAUSE OF THE POKINESS OF LIGHT, AND BECAUSE UTILITARIA IS SEVERAL LIGHT-WEEKS FROM EARTH, THE UTILITARIANS ARE DOOMED THROUGHOUT ALL ETERNITY TO SEE ONLY RE-RUNS...

Panel 9: AND GUESS WHAT? THE LAG TIME JUST HAPPENS TO STRETCH BACK TO A PERIOD WHEN OUR FAVORITE HAS-BEEN WAS HOGGING UP THE AIRWAVES...

Panel 10: THE RESULT IS FAR TOO HORRIBLE AN AESTHETIC ABERRATION TO DEPICT HERE. PARENTS ARE STRONGLY URGED TO USE DISCRETION WHEN SHOWING THIS LAST PANEL TO THEIR CHILDREN.

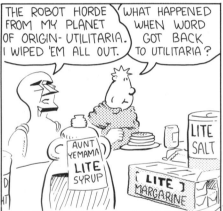

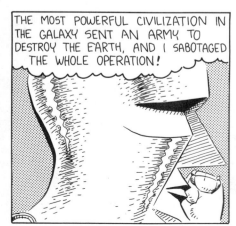

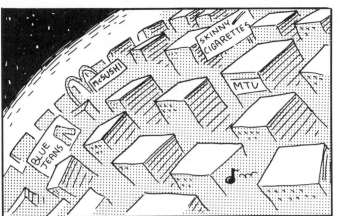

Q: WHY DO UTILITARIANS JUMP ALL OVER THEMSELVES IN FAWNING ADHERENCE TO EVERY PASSING EARTH TREND?

A: THE PLANET UTILITARIA HAS A CRUSH ON THE PLANET EARTH...

EYEBEAM

YOU KNOW, STYLE IS AN ELUSIVE CONCEPT, BUT I STILL BELIEVE IN TIMELESS, UNIVERSAL STANDARDS.

REALLY? IT SEEMS LIKE WHATEVER IS **IN** ALWAYS ENDS UP BEING **OUT** SOONER OR LATER...

YEAH, BUT THERE ARE COMMERCIAL REASONS BEHIND THAT—THEY HAVE TO PUT OUT SOMETHING DIFFERENT EVERY YEAR SO PEOPLE WILL EVENTUALLY BE FORCED TO BUY A NEW PRODUCT.

...BUT THEN THE PENDULUM FINALLY SWINGS BACK, EH?

RIGHT. THAT'S WHEN THEY'LL BRING BACK FINS ON CARS.

ALL **RIGHT!**

PUT PUT PUT-

WHAT DID HE SAY? THAT **JERK!** I **HATE** IT WHEN SOMEONE MAKES FUN OF MY CAR!

RELAX, RATLIFF. THEY'RE JUST JEALOUS.

YEAH. THIS IS A COLLECTOR'S ITEM.

I'LL BET THEY WISH **THEY** WERE DRIVING A VINTAGE 1952 SCROD.

THEY JUST DON'T MAKE 'EM LIKE THIS ANYMORE!

ACTUALLY, RATLIFF, THEY NEVER **DID**...

WELL, I'VE **WONDERED** ABOUT THAT...

39

PIG IN A BLANKET... HEAD IN THE SAND...

WE'RE NOT INCLINED TO TRUST IN THINGS WE CANNOT UNDERSTAND.

FLINTSTONE VITAMINS

ASHES TO ASHES...

DUST TO DUST...

WHY DON'T WE ALL ADMIT WE LIVE IN MORTAL FEAR OF RUST.

MAN HAS ALWAYS BEEN FASCINATED BY THE SEA...

PERHAPS FOR SOME, IT STEMS FROM A PRIMAL URGE TO RETURN TO THEIR SPAWN.

OTHERS SEE A METAPHOR FOR THE OVERWHELMING POWER OF NATURE...

THEN THERE ARE THOSE OF US WHO JUST PLAIN LOOK BOSS IN A BATHINGSUIT.

HE MAY BE A MACHINE, BUT HE SEEMS CAPABLE OF ABSTRACT THOUGHT.

43

FAR BELOW, ON THE SMOOTHLY-PACKED EARTHEN PATHS, THE NATIVES SHUDDER SILENTY...

...FOR THEY KNOW THAT SHE-GIRL, QUEEN OF THE LEOPARDS, GLIDES LIKE A SHADOW THROUGH THE DENSE JUNGLE CANOPY ABOVE.

BUT THEY NEED NOT FEAR, FOR TONIGHT SHE STALKS AN OUTSIDER—A POACHING WHITE HUNTER.

I DON'T KNOW—MAYBE I NEED A NAP...

THE CODE OF JUNGLE JUSTICE IS HARSH BUT FAIR.

¡@#!

I JUST REALIZED WE HAVE **FOUR** ROBOTS SHACKING UP IN OUR GUEST ROOM!

HAVE WE BECOME SO ENRAPTURED WITH TECHNOLOGY THAT WE'VE LOST TOUCH WITH THAT WHICH MAKES US HUMAN?

FOUR ROBOTS AND THE GUY GOES APE. I TAKE IT HE'S NEVER BEEN TO A CONVENTION.

I GUESS NOT.

EYE BEAM

Panel 1:
"YOU'RE THE GUY WITH "SALIVA & SLOTH," RIGHT?"

"YES. I CAME BY BECAUSE I'M VERY INTERESTED IN YOUR FISH CASE..."

Panel 2:
"WELL, COURTS DON'T TEND TO RECOGNIZE FISH ISSUES. THE ONLY PRECEDENT I'VE FOUND IS ANIMAL RIGHTS GROUPS SUING ON BEHALF OF LABORATORY TEST ANIMALS."

"SPEAKING OF PRECEDENTS, I WISH YOU LUCK— IT MIGHT HELP WITH A CASE I'M PREPARING."

Panel 3:
"A CASE YOU'RE PREPARING?"

"A CLASS ACTION ON BEHALF OF "ROACHES FOR A TRUE DEMOCRACY"..."

Panel 4:
"WELL, HERE WE ARE... HOME SWEET HOME..."

"HURRY UP, MAN! MY FINS ARE GETTING TIRED!"

Panel 5:
"HOW DO YOU DO THAT, ANYWAY?"

"WELL, THIS STUFF IS SO SLIPPERY, IT'S A MATTER OF STRUGGLING AND STRAINING AS HARD AS I CAN JUST TO STAY IN ONE PLACE..."

Panel 6:
"GEE, HOW POIGNANT... SORT OF A METAPHOR FOR LIFE ITSELF..."

"JUST OPEN THE FISHHOOKING DOOR!"

EYEBEAM

EYEBEAM

EYEBEAM, I'VE GOT THIS REALLY INTENSE CRUSH ON BETH...

BETH!? YOU MEAN **ROD'S GIRLFRIEND** BETH?

YES. UNFORTUNATELY, THAT'S THE ONE I MEAN.

GIRLFRIEND OF "MR. SHOULDERS OUT TO HERE"?

THIS IS VERY SERIOUS. MY LIFE HAS BECOME MEANINGLESS WITHOUT HER.

OK. OK. SO, WHAT ARE YOU GONNA DO?

LOOK AT THIS— THE MADE-FOR-TV MOVIES GET STUPIDER ALL THE TIME!

YEAH, THAT'S ABOUT WHAT I'D DO.

IS SOMEBODY HERE? I THOUGHT I HEARD A CAR PULL UP.

I'LL BET IT'S BETH.

HOW COULD YOU POSSIBLY KNOW THAT?

EVER SEE A PUPPY DOG BEING LOWERED INTO A VAT OF WARM BACON FAT?

ANYBODY HOME?

EYEBEAM

MANY MILES HAVE I TRAVELED, MANY DANGERS HAVE I CONFRONTED...

ALL TO LAY THIS UNWORTHY TROPHY AT YOUR GLORIOUS FEET. I ASK IN RETURN MERELY THAT YOU ACKNOWLEDGE MY MEASLY EXISTENCE.

I'M AFRAID THIS COULD BE SERIOUS...

HIGH ABOVE THE PLANET'S SURFACE SOARS A GOD-LIKE WORK OF ART, HEWN NOT FROM COLD MARBLE, BUT FROM THE FINEST QUALITY SIZZLING PRIME BEEF...

66

ITS... HONKMAN!

DON'T WORRY, GIRLS. IT'LL TAKE A WHILE, BUT I'LL GET TO ALL OF YOU.

SIGH... GASP... AH! SWOON! YOW

AW SHOOT. JUST WHEN I THOUGHT I'D FINALLY MET THE THRONG OF MY DREAMS.

EYEBEAM, I'VE JUST GOTTA SPILL MY GUTS...

HEY, **WHOAH!** THE MEN'S ROOM IS OVER THERE...

IT'S SERIOUS. AN OLD FRIEND OF MINE IS COMING TO TOWN..

UH OH... THAT **DOES** SOUND SERIOUS!

IT **IS**. WHEN YOU HAVE MY HIGH DEGREE OF SELF-CONFIDENCE, IT'S VERY DISTURBING TO BE AROUND SOMEONE YOU LOOK UP TO AND RESPECT.

WHO **IS** THIS GUY, ANYWAY?

WELL, HIS NAME IS LANCE TROUSERS...

SOMEHOW, I FEEL I KNOW HIM ALREADY.

EYEBEAM, I REALLY AM WORRIED ABOUT LANCE TROUSERS COMING TO TOWN. WHAT IF HE SNATCHES AWAY THE JEWEL OF MY LIFE?

THE GUY'S A FRIEND. I THINK YOUR CAR IS SAFE.

I MEAN **BETH**! LANCE WAS ALWAYS THE KING! GIRLS MELTED INTO INCOHERENT PRIMATES AROUND HIM...

AW... I'LL BET YOUR MEMORIES OF HIM ARE EXAGGERATED A BIT.

YOU MAY BE RIGHT. ALSO, TIME HAS PROBABLY TAKEN ITS TOLL ON HIS SKILLS...

BESIDES, BETH HAS TOO MUCH WILLPOWER TO FALL FOR SOME STUDLY STRANGER...

▶ MEANWHILE... ◀

HELLO. I'M A FRIEND OF ROD'S. IS HE AROUND?

YOW! ARF...

73

EYEBEAM

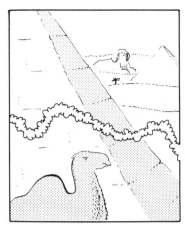

79

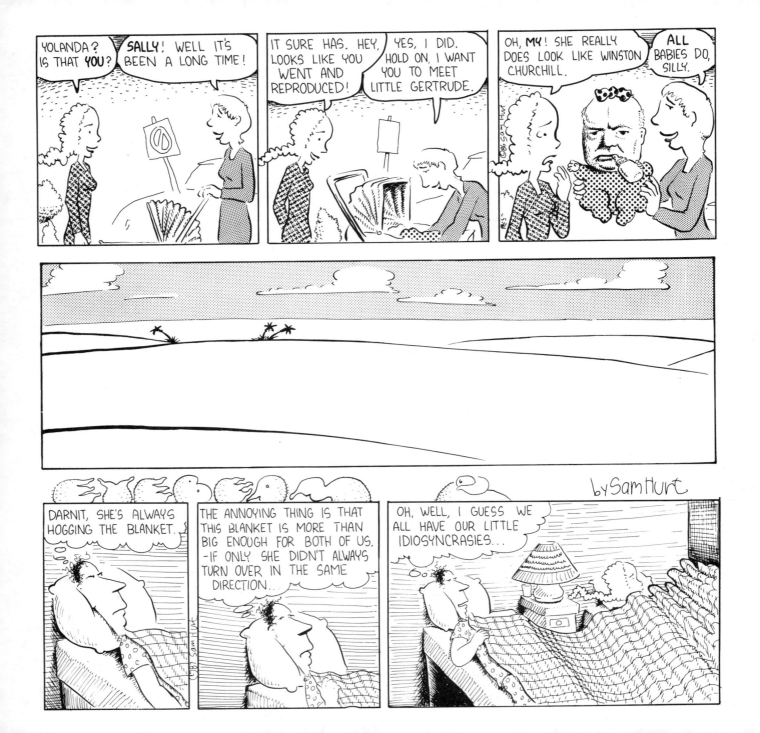

EYEBEAM

Panel 1:
THE WILDEBEEST FREEZES, INSTINCTIVELY SENSING DANGER - BUT IT IS ALREADY FAR TOO LATE...

Panel 2:
THE WAYS OF NATURE OFTEN SEEM CRUEL, BUT THEY ALWAYS SHOW A COLD-BLOODED ECONOMY OF PURPOSE: THE SHE-PANTHER DOESN'T FINISH-OFF THE WILDEBEEST IMMEDIATELY, BUT "PLAYS" WITH IT TO SHARPEN HER PREDATORY SKILLS.

SHOOTING
STABBING

Panel 3:

HAVE YOU SEEN TODAY'S PAPER, EYEBEAM?

IN THERE. I HOPE YOU HAVE A STRONG STOMACH.

Panel 4:

Panel 5:

IT **WOULD** BE A NICE DAY FOR A CRUISE; IF IT WEREN'T FOR CERTAIN ANNOYING DISTRACTIONS...

YARF YARF YARF

Panel 6:

I SUPPOSE I COULD JUST PUT UP WITH IT... IN THE SPIRIT OF COMPROMISE..

YARF SNAP

Panel 7:

BUT DARNIT, TODAY I JUST SEEM TO FEEL **UN**COMPROMISING.

YIPE!

92

93

...YAWN. THIS BANKRUPTCY SEMINAR IS ABOUT TO PUT MY ATTENTION SPAN INTO CHAPTER 11...

C'MON! - WAKE UP! THERE'S A REASON YOU'RE HERE -- SO YOU CAN COMPETENTLY ADVISE YOUR CLIENTS ABOUT BANKRUPTCY...

AFTER ALL, THIS STUFF IS PROBABLY FASCINATING ONCE YOU GET INTO IT...

I'LL BET IT OWN ZZZZZZZZZZ

AS YOUR ATTORNEY, I ADVISE YOU TO STAY RICH...

WHEN I WAS LITTLE, I'D DREAM OF CLIMBING ON TOP OF THE HOUSE AND TOUCHING THE CLOUDS. TOUCHING YOU HAS THE SAME MAGIC, EXCEPT I DON'T FALL DOWN THE CHIMNEY AFTERWARDS...

I WISH THIS MOMENT COULD LAST FOREVER,... OF COURSE, THEN IT WOULDN'T BE A MOMENT ANYMORE...

THE LIGHT IN YOUR EYES- I'D LIKE TO PUT IT IN A TUBE, TAKE IT HOME, AND RUB IT ON MY TUMMY...

ME NEXT! I'LL BRING THEIR CHECK!

NO FAIR! - I HAVEN'T BEEN YET

94

EYEBEAM

NOW, WHERE DID THAT AMBERCROMBIE BRIEF GO?

THERE IT IS... HOW DID IT GET WAY OVER THERE?

HEY- WHAT THE-?

IT LOOKS LIKES HANK IS UP TO HIS CHILDISH PRANKS **AGAIN.**

CAN EYEBEAM COME OUT AND PLAY?

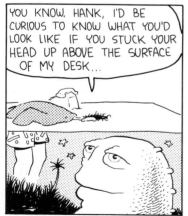

YOU KNOW, HANK, I'D BE CURIOUS TO KNOW WHAT YOU'D LOOK LIKE IF YOU STUCK YOUR HEAD UP ABOVE THE SURFACE OF MY DESK...

...EVER HAVE ONE OF THOSE DAYS WHERE NOTHING MUCH GETS ACCOMPLISHED?

...NGH...

SPLOP

OH, NO! IT'S THAT DAMN ABERNATHY FILE!

WELCOME TO THE REAL WORLD..

I'LL COME BACK LATER... I SEE YOU'RE SWAMPED RIGHT NOW...

99

EYEBEAM

THE ROAD OF LIFE
HAS BEEN UPHILL;
I'VE STRUGGLED ALL THE WAY.

-TO TOW THE LINE,
-TO FILL THE BILL,
-TO EARN MY WEEKLY PAY.
AND EARN I HAVE.
MY ASSETS NOW
COULD PAY A NATION'S DEBT...

I'M BLESSED WITH LOVED-
ONES TO ENDOW;
I GIVE WITH JOY, AND YET-
IF LIFE IS TRULY LIKE A PATH,
AND LIKE ALL THINGS MUST
END...

..I GUESS I'LL
REALLY TAKE
A BATH
UPON THAT
FINAL BEND.

CAN WE GET
ON TO THE
NUTS AND
BOLTS OF
THIS?

EYEBEAM

PEACHES, I'M GOING TO THE
STORE FOR A WHILE. NOW, JUST
PLAY IN THE YARD AND BE
A **GOOD** GIRL WHILE I'M
GONE.

YOU HEAR ME, RIGHT?
YOU'LL BE **GOOD**, RIGHT?
YOU'RE NOT GOING TO
CAUSE ANY **MISCHIEF**
NOW, ARE YOU?..

GEEZE! SETTLE
DOWN, UNCLE
RATLIFF! IT'S
NOT THAT BIG
A DEAL...

I MEAN, WHAT DOES
HE THINK COULD
HAPPEN, ANYWAY?

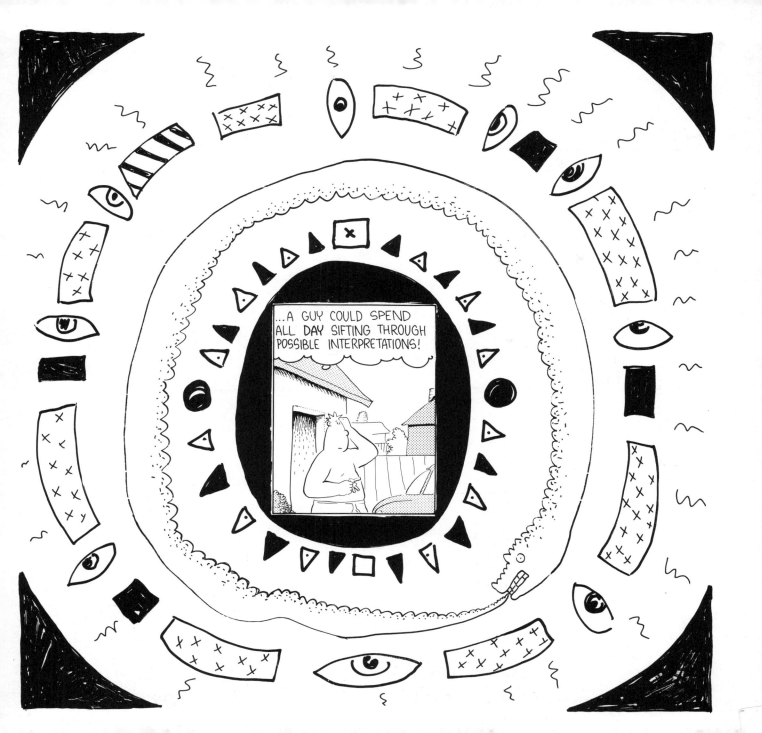

EYEBEAM

Project your own mind's EYEBEAM comic strip
onto this page. Specially treated paper will make
it actually appear in 3 to 6 hours.

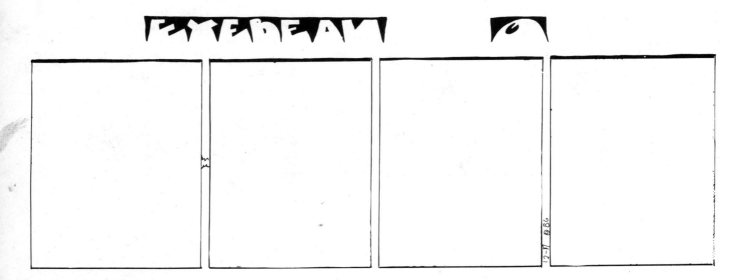